BRIEF GUIDE

TO

THE DEPARTMENT
OF ANCIENT ART

THE BROOKLYN MUSEUM
BROOKLYN, N.Y.
1970

The Brooklyn Museum Guide Number 5
by
Bernard V. Bothmer and Jean L. Keith

Library of Congress Catalog Card Number: 71-138275
Printed by Verlag Philipp von Zabern
Mainz, West-Germany

CONTENTS

MINI TOUR

The hurried visitor who merely wishes to take in the highlights, not necessarily in chronological order, may proceed as follows:

Gallery 10:   Assyrian reliefs, silver treasure from Tell el Maskhuta

Gallery 9:   Granite sarcophagus, royal head in niche

Gallery 6:   Bird deities, ivory knife handle

Gallery 7:   Bronze falcon, faience Aphrodite

Gallery 8:   Temple gate model, the "Brooklyn Black Head"

Gallery 5:   Wooden cat, silver ibis

Gallery 4:   Royal sculptures of Dynasty VI

Galleries 4,9:   Methethy's wooden statues

Gallery 3:   Wooden panel with mosaic glass inlays, turquoise-blue faiences

Gallery 2:   Sphinx head, Amarna reliefs

Gallery 1:   Recent acquisitions

Gallery 12:   Greek gold

Gallery 11-E: Coptic lunette, Hercules with the bull

Gallery 11-N: Mummy portraits, textile hanging

Gallery 11-W: Jewish mosaics, head of Alexander

Gallery 11-S: Cycladic figures, Minoan vase

CHRONOLOGY

	EGYPT	PALESTINE AND SYRIA	MESOPOTAMIA	IRAN	ANATOLIA	AEGEAN	GREECE
4000	·········4000········· PREDYNASTIC PERIOD Amratian (Nagada I) Gerzean (Nagada II)						
3500		·······3500······· CHALCOLITHIC PERIOD	·······3500······· URUK PERIOD	Village farming Painted Pottery Cultures SUSA C Contacts with Meso- potamia and Egypt	NEOLITHIC-CHALCO- LITHIC PERIODS ·······3500·······	LATE NEOLITHIC PERIOD ·······3300·······	LATE NEOLITHIC PERIOD ·······3300·······
3000	·······3100······· EARLY DYNASTIC (ARCHAIC) PERIOD Dynasties I and II	·······3100······· EARLY BRONZE AGE I	·······3100······· JAMDAT NASR PERIOD ·······2900······· EARLY DYNASTIC PERIODS I-III Rivalry between Sumerian city-states Royal Cemetery at Ur		EARLY BRONZE AGE	*Cycladic Idols* 2800–2000 EARLY HELLADIC I EARLY MINOAN I E.H. II E.M. II E.H. III E.M. III	*Cycladic Idols* 2800-2000 EARLY HELLADIC I (Mainland Greece) EARLY MINOAN I (Crete)
2500	·······2686······· OLD KINGDOM Dynasty III 2686-2613 Dynasty IV 2613-2494 Dynasty V 2494-2345 Dynasty VI 2345-2181	E.B. II Egyptian contacts with Byblos		SUSA D			·········2400·········
			·······2371······· AKKAD PERIOD ·······2230······· POST-AKKAD PERIOD 2230-2130 THIRD DYNASTY OF UR 2113-2006	Akkadian domination of Susa	Troy Level II c. 2500-2300 *Treasure of Troy* c. 2300 Royal Burials at Alaça Hüyük	E.H. II E.M. II ·······2200······· E.H. III E.M. III ·······2000·······	
2000	·······2181······· FIRST INTERMEDIATE PERIOD Dynasties VII-X	E.B. III		OLD ELAMITE PERIOD			·······2000······· EARLY PALACE PERIOD (Crete)

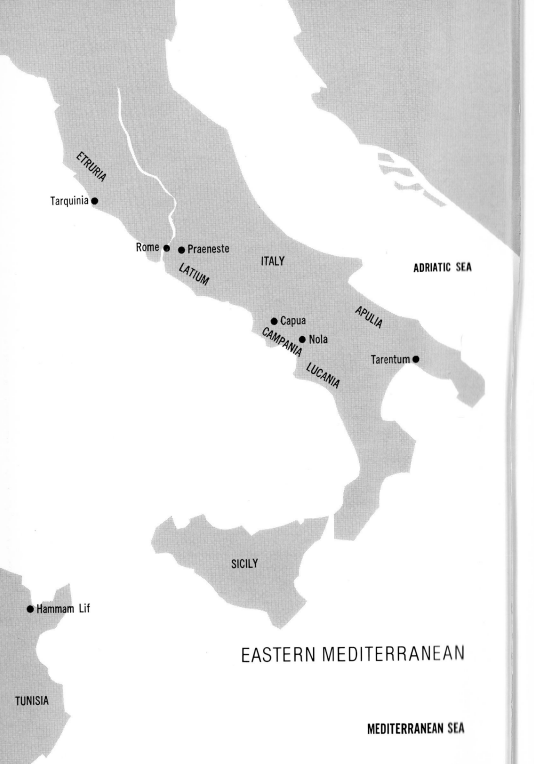

EASTERN MEDITERRANEAN

MEDITERRANEAN SEA

	EGYPT	PALESTINE AND SYRIA	MESOPOTAMIA	IRAN	ANATOLIA	AEGEAN	GREECE
2000	----2040---- MIDDLE KINGDOM Dyn. XI 2134-1991 Dyn. XII					EARLY PALACE PERIOD Minoan MIDDLE HELLADIC PERIOD	
	----1785---- SECOND INTER-MEDIATE PERIOD Dyn. XIII 1785-1544 Dyn. XIV 1750-1554 (Hyksos Rulers)	MIDDLE BRONZE II	----1792---- OLD BABYLONIAN PERIOD Hammurabi 1792-50		----1740---- OLD HITTITE KINGDOM	----1700---- LATE PALACE PERIOD 1700-1400 Minoan EARLY MYCENAEAN	----1700---- LATE PALACE PERIOD 1700-1400 (Crete) EARLY MYCENAEAN
1500	----1554---- NEW KINGDOM Dynasty XVIII 1554-1320 Amarna 1378-1355 Dynasty XIX 1320-1200 Dynasty XX 1200-1087	----1550---- LATE BRONZE AGE Canaanite and Amorite City-states Exodus Philistines Arameans	----1595---- MITANNI AND KASSITE PERIODS ----1350---- MIDDLE ASSYRIAN PERIOD	MIDDLE ELAMITE PERIOD	----1460---- HITTITE EMPIRE ----1200----	PERIOD 1600-1400 Mainland LATE MYCENAEAN PERIOD 1400 — ca. 1200	PERIOD 1600-1400 (Mainland) MYCENAEAN 1400-1200
				NEO-ELAMITE PERIOD	PHRYGIAN STATES LATE HITTITE STATES	----1100---- Dorian Invasions	----1100---- Dorian Infiltrations
1000	----1087---- THIRD INTERMEDIATE PERIOD Dynasties XXI-XXIV	----1020---- HEBREW KINGDOM ----950---- LATE HITTITE AND ARAMEAN STATES Phoenicians Assyrian conquest	----1020---- NEO-ASSYRIAN EMPIRE (in the North)	Ziwiyeh 800-600 Luristan 12th-7th cent. — metalwork		----1000---- PROTOGEOMETRIC PERIOD ----850---- GEOMETRIC PERIOD	----1000---- PROTOGEOMETRIC and GEOMETRIC PERIODS ----800---- ORIENTALIZING PERIOD
	----715---- LATE PERIOD Dyn. XXV 728-656 Kushite Period Dyn. XXVI 664-525 Saite Period Dyn. XXVII 525-404 Persian Period Dyn. XXVIII-XXIX 404-378 Dyn. XXX 378-341 Dyn. XXXI 341-333	----612---- ACHAEMENID PERSIAN EMPIRE	NEO-BABYLONIAN PERIOD (in the South) ----539---- ACHAEMENID PERSIAN EMPIRE	----700---- ACHAEMENIDS 700-330 Medes 625-550	----700---- LYDIAN KINGDOM ----546---- ACHAEMENID PERSIAN EMPIRE	----720---- ORIENTALIZING PERIOD ----620---- ARCHAIC PERIOD ----490---- TRANSITIONAL PERIOD ----470---- CLASSICAL PERIOD	----600---- ARCHAIC PERIOD ----500---- CLASSICAL PERIOD ----420---- LATE CLASSICAL PERIOD
500			----330---- the Great Seleucid Rule HELLENISTIC PERIOD		----330---- HELLENISTIC PERIOD	----330---- HELLENISTIC PERIOD	----330---- Alexander the Great HELLENISTIC PERIOD ROMAN RULE
	HELLENISTIC RULE IN EGYPT Macedonian Period 332-304 Ptolemaic Period 304-30 ----30 B.C.---- ROMAN PERIOD	----330---- Alexander the Great HELLENISTIC PERIOD ----63 B.C.---- ROMAN PERIOD	----171 B.C.---- PARTHIAN RULE	----250 B.C.---- PARTHIAN EMPIRE	----133 B.C.---- ROMAN PERIOD		
1							

Map labels:
ETRURIA
Tarquinia ●
Rome ● ● Praeneste
LATIUM
ITALY
ADRIATIC SEA
● Capua
APULIA
CAMPANIA ● Nola
LUCANIA
Tarentum ●
SICILY
● Hammam Lif
TUNISIA

MEDITERRANEAN SEA

EGYPT

Alexandria ●
Sais ●
  DELTA
Naucratis ●
● Tanis
● Mendes
Leontopolis ●
Pithom ●
● Suez
Giza ●
● Cairo
SINAI
Mitrahineh (Memphis) ●
Saqqara ●
The Fayum
● Lisht
● Meidum
Oxyrhynchos ●
Hermopolis Magna ●
● Antinoopolis
● Tell el Amarna
● Akhmim
Wadi Hammamat
Abydos ●
● Koptos
Naqada ●
● Luxor
Thebes
Armant ●
● Karnak
RED SEA
Hierakonpolis ●
Edfu ●
● Assuan
Nile River
NUBIA
KUSH

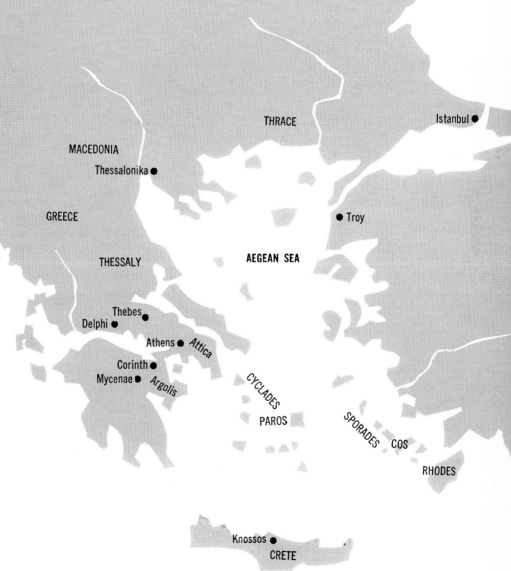

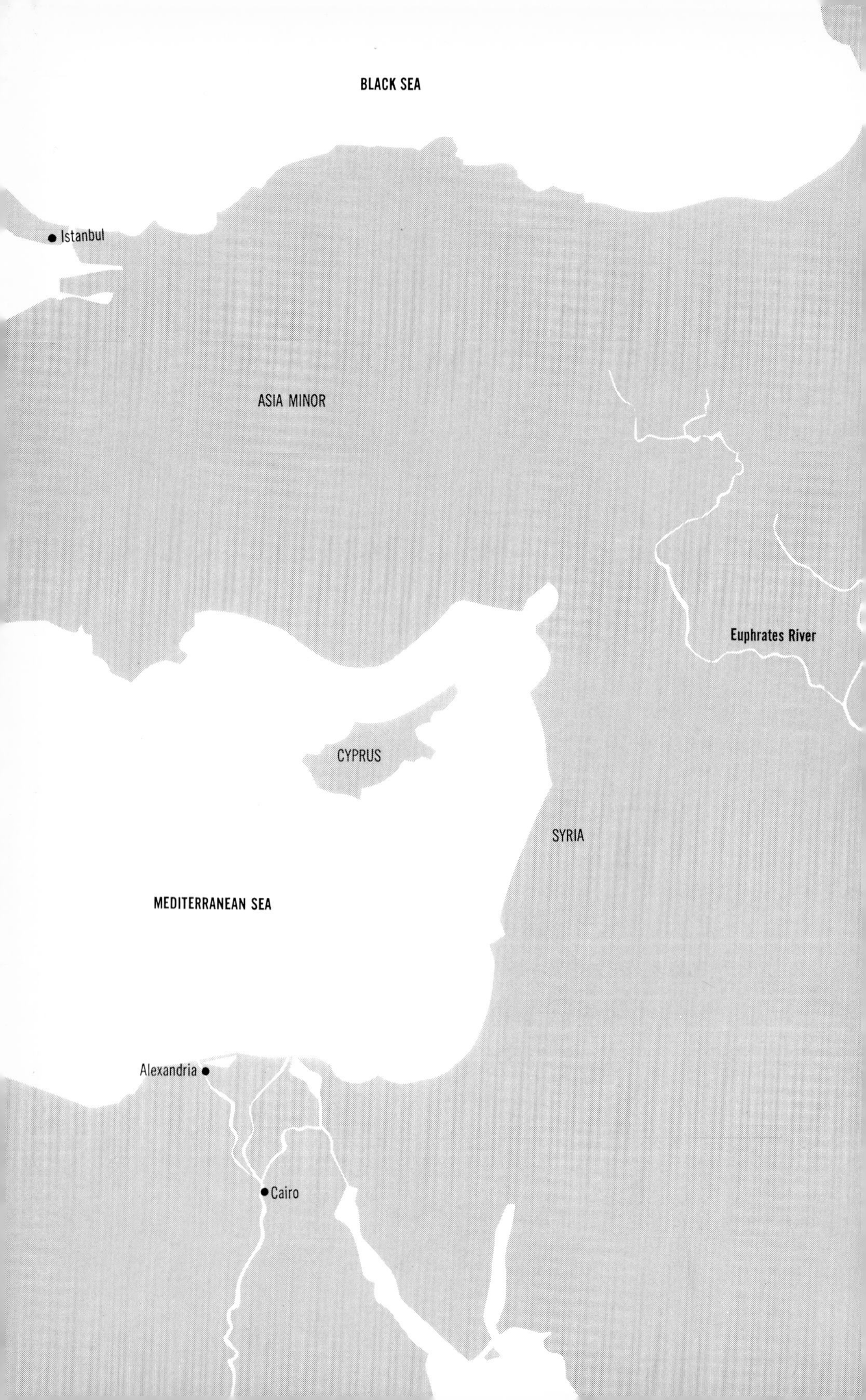

BLACK SEA

● Istanbul

ASIA MINOR

Euphrates River

CYPRUS

SYRIA

MEDITERRANEAN SEA

Alexandria ●

● Cairo

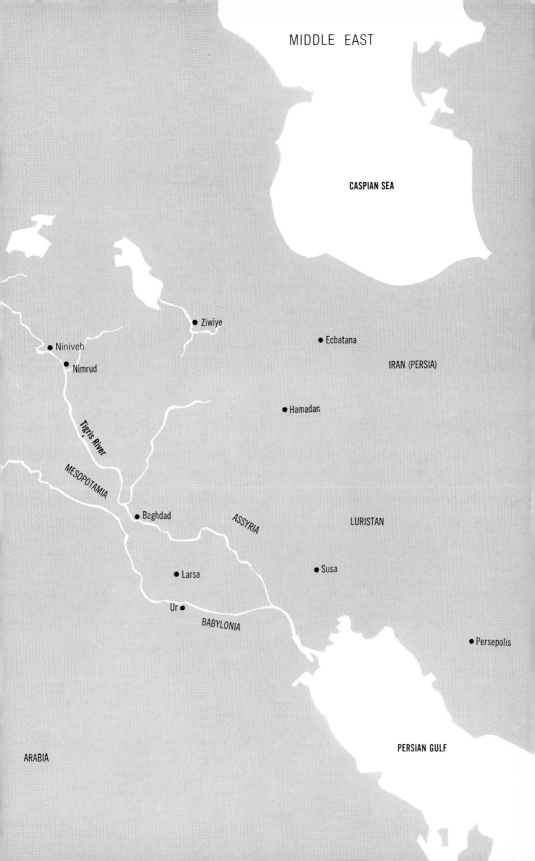

INTRODUCTION

The Department of Ancient Art on the Third Floor of the Museum consists of major Egyptian and Coptic collections, a Middle Eastern collection, and a Graeco-Roman collection. Originally the Department formed a division of the Museum's Department of Fine Arts; in 1932 it was listed as the "Department of Antiquities" and in 1933 as "Department of Egyptian and Classical Art." The Department of Ancient Art has borne its present name since 1934, when it consisted of an "Egyptian Division" and a "Classical Division." The latter was listed in 1935 as the "Greek and Roman Section."

The strength of the Department lies primarily in the collection of Egyptian art, not among the largest but certainly among the finest in the world. From very small beginnings, this collection has reached preeminence in the course of a scant half century.

Although some odds and ends from the Nile Valley may already have found their way to the Museum during the late 1800's, the first objects from ancient Egypt to be recorded in the Department's files were acquired in 1902. They were purchased on behalf of The Brooklyn Museum by none other than the great English Egyptologist Flinders Petrie who continued to make acquisitions in Egypt for the Museum for about a decade.

With the growth of the Museum, interest in the art and archaeology of ancient Egypt increased rapidly in Brooklyn, and as a result a field expedition was undertaken. This was entrusted to the French prehistorian Henri de Morgan (1854-1909) who for two seasons, 1906-1907 and 1907-1908, conducted a highly successful survey of various Predynastic sites in Upper Egypt, acquiring objects for the Museum through excavation and local purchase. Consequently Brooklyn owns several unique specimens which go back to the end of the fifth or the beginning of the fourth millennium B.C., centuries before the "dawn of history."

In 1908 the Egyptian collection of Armand De Potter was acquired. This group, formed in the eighties at the time of the great finds in the Theban necropolis at Deir el Bahari, brought to the Museum its first mummy and first coffin. From 1912 until 1939, the collections were augmented by a trickle of objects from the excava-

1

tions of the Egypt Exploration Fund (since 1919 called the Egypt Exploration Society) which were assigned to the Museum in return for contributions made toward the work of that organization. Although a few Coptic textiles came to Brooklyn as early as 1905, the addition, in 1915, of several dozen pieces from the excavations of the Egypt Exploration Fund at Antinoöpolis marked the beginning of what has grown to be probably in this country the most extensive assemblage of Coptic art, that is, native Egyptian art from the time of the Roman domination and the early centuries following the Arab conquest — an art that includes and sometimes mingles motifs of Hellenistic paganism and those of emerging Christianity (see pp. 96 ff.).

The following year, 1916, became a milestone in the history of the Department. It was in that year that the library and collection of Charles Edwin Wilbour (1833-1896) were given to the Museum by his children, Evangeline Wilbour Blashfield, Theodora Wilbour, and Victor Wilbour, following a wish of their mother, Charlotte Beebe Wilbour, who had asked before her death in 1914 that the books and antiquities belonging to her late husband be given to a public institution in the United States, as a memorial of their father.

Charles Edwin Wilbour was born in Little Compton, R. I., in 1833, attended Brown University, was admitted to the bar, became a court reporter in New York and subsequently, as president of the New York Printing Company, was publisher of *The (New York Daily) Transcript*, the only daily legal newspaper of his time.

In 1874, because of setbacks in his political career, Wilbour sailed for Europe, where he resumed his early studies in the humanities, but soon specialized in the then new academic field of Egyptology. After attending courses in France and Germany — and avidly collecting books on ancient Egypt — he went, in 1880, to Egypt, and from that time until his death he spent every winter on the Nile, visiting the monuments and studying their inscriptions. The summers were passed in Europe and at the family home in Rhode Island. He died in Paris in 1896.

Wilbour was a man of wide learning. He was greatly respected by his colleagues in Europe and in Egypt, among whom were numbered

2

many of the great scholars of the nineteenth century. His library must have been one of the finest private libraries of his time, and in addition to books he also assembled over two thousand Egyptian antiquities. Although most of these were small and primarily of archaeological interest, he acquired a few fine pieces and, above all, an outstanding collection of papyri and ostraca.

Part of his collection came to the Museum after the initial bequest in 1916; it was not until 1947, when the last of his daughters died, that the Museum received a final lot of papyri. Among other treasures this lot included a great hoard of Aramaic papyri of the fifth century B.C. which had been found at Elephantine, folded and sealed as they had been filed away over two thousand years ago. It is the largest single collection of its kind in the Western world.

Although the Aramaic papyri were published in 1953, the wealth of unique documents among the other Wilbour papyri is so great that it will take many years to publish in full the mass of hieratic, demotic, and Greek texts which they contain.

Victor Wilbour, only son of Charles Edwin Wilbour, died unmarried in 1931. In a last will and testament drawn up in 1922, Victor Wilbour stipulated that his residuary estate "to be known as the Charles Edwin Wilbour Fund," be turned over to the Brooklyn Institute of Arts and Sciences, of which The Brooklyn Museum is a department. The income of this Fund was to be used "for the purpose of maintaining and adding to and developing the Egyptological Collection and Library . . ."

This large sum, received in 1932, enabled the Museum to install the Wilbour Collection, together with Egyptian objects from other sources, in the great east gallery on the north side of the Third Floor. This gallery was dedicated on May 30, 1933, as the Charles Edwin Wilbour Memorial Hall. In the course of the following year Wilbour's library was shelved in the northeast corner of the Third Floor in a small gallery specially remodeled by George Howe and William Lescaze to receive it and the small collection of Egyptological works that had been acquired by the Museum over the years. Wilbour's library, when it came to Brooklyn, contained nearly every nineteenth century

3

publication on ancient Egypt. From 2500 items in 1916 it has grown tenfold; it forms the greatest single scholarly asset of the Museum and, kept up to date, is now one of the three best Egyptological libraries in the world. It was opened in its present quarters on November 23, 1934, as the Charles Edwin Wilbour Memorial Library of Egyptology.

Most important of all, the Wilbour Fund permitted the Museum to engage a staff qualified to fulfill the terms of Victor Wilbour's bequest. As a first step in this direction, a well-known Belgian scholar, Professor Jean Capart (1877-1947), head of the Egyptian collection in Brussels and director of the Fondation Egyptologique Reine Elisabeth in that city, was invited to come to Brooklyn on a part-time basis as Honorary Curator of Egyptology. He arrived in February 1932 and for six years Professor Capart annually visited the United States, acting as a consultant in Brooklyn and lecturing there and elsewhere on Egyptological subjects.

Capart was a dynamic personality. He had an impressive bibliographical knowledge, a boundless enthusiasm for Egyptology and a rare capacity for imparting it. Through lecturing, writing, and extensive social activity he stimulated public interest in ancient Egypt not only in his own country but in Brooklyn and elsewhere in the United States. He had, however, little real feeling for quality in works of art, small knowledge of the art market, and no realization of the needs of a growing collection; the multiplicity of his activities left him little time for training a Brooklyn staff.

The objects he recommended for purchase to the Trustees of the Museum were with few exceptions of archaeological or historical interest but small artistic value. He made, however, two major contributions to the Department. The first was the acquisition of a great papyrus of late Ramesside date, a vast document dealing with the measurements and assessment of fields. This unique record of land holdings in ancient Egypt was named after Charles Edwin Wilbour and, thanks to its masterly publication in four volumes (1941-1952) by Sir Alan Gardiner, has become one of the most frequently cited economic papyri. Only after acquisition of this papyrus in 1935 and

4

1947 did the majority of the great papyri collected by Wilbour himself come to Brooklyn.

Capart's second major achievement was the publication of Wilbour's *Travels in Egypt* (1936), a collection of letters which Wilbour wrote almost daily from Egypt to members of his family in Paris and in the United States, between December 1880 and May 1891. These letters provide a lively picture of life on the Nile during a great period of discovery. They comment on historic finds, on collecting and copying, and on famous scholars and travelers with whom Wilbour often had an exciting exchange of ideas. Although this book drew attention to Wilbour 40 years after his death, a much vaster collection of his notes on Egyptian sites and antiquities and of his copies of unpublished inscriptions yet remains to be brought out in print.

Professor Capart paid his last visit to Brooklyn in the Fall of 1938 but was carried on the staff list of the Museum as Honorary Advisory Curator until his death in 1947. During his incumbency, the day-by-day functioning of the Department was assured by an Assistant Curator. The first to hold this position was Edwin L. M. Taggart, who served from 1932 to 1936. In 1933 he published a *Short Guide to the Charles Edwin Wilbour Egyptological Collection*. It was left, however, to John D. Cooney (Harvard '32) to bring into order a large and motly assemblage of antiquities and to transform it by judicious purchases into a major collection of Egyptian art.

In 1934, after graduate work at Harvard, Mr. Cooney joined the staff of the Museum. He was appointed Assistant Curator of Egyptology in the Fall of 1936 and two years later, having meantime continued his studies at the University of Pennsylvania, he was made Curator of the Department of Ancient Art.

Since Mr. Cooney found the collection largely unrecorded, he was obliged to spend a great part of his early years at the Museum in departmental housework. This routine labor was intensified in 1937 with the arrival of a collection of some 2000 antiquities given as an indefinite loan by the New-York Historical Society to The Brooklyn Museum, every one of which had to be separately listed. In 1948 these antiquities became by purchase part of the Museum's permanent collection.

The objects had come in the mid-nineteenth century to the New-York Historical Society which now wished to divest itself of material not pertinent to the history of the City and the State of New York. The collection included a series of large Assyrian reliefs, known then as the Lenox Collection of Nineveh Sculptures, but mainly consisted of well over 2000 Egyptian antiquities. It was speedily put on exhibition on the east side of the Third Floor, in a large gallery (later converted into a lecture hall), and there it remained for something over a decade.

Unlike Wilbour's collection, that from the New-York Historical Society contained a number of large pieces and many of fine quality. The Egyptian objects had been assembled from a number of sources, chief among them a collection formed well before the middle of the nineteenth century by Dr. Henry Abbott (1812-1859), an Englishman resident in Egypt. Dr. Abbott brought his collection to New York in 1853 for exhibition at the Stuyvesant Institute at 659 Broadway, and in 1860 it was acquired by the New-York Historical Society. It is a remarkable collection, reflecting almost every aspect of Egyptian art, and although it has a number of gaps and contains a few nineteenth-century forgeries, its acquisition brought Brooklyn a long way toward becoming a major repository for fine works from ancient Egypt. Mr. Cooney's keen eye and unfailing judgment finally carried the Egyptian collection into a position of first quality. He headed the Department until 1963 when he resigned to become Curator of Egyptian and Classical Art at The Cleveland Museum of Art.

In 1937, Mrs. Elizabeth Riefstahl was appointed Librarian of the Charles Edwin Wilbour Memorial Library. Although a meticulous catalogue of the Wilbour books had been compiled by William Burt Cook, Jr. and published by the Museum in 1924, most of the books in the Library had never been systematically catalogued. Mrs. Riefstahl retired after nineteen years of service, having brought order out of chaos, and in the dozen years since her retirement a series of able librarians has continued the work of expansion and cataloguing.

After her appointment as Wilbour Librarian, Mrs. Riefstahl gradually became interested in the work of the Department. During World War II, when Mr. Cooney was serving in the Army, she carried on the work of both Department and Library and was rewarded with the title of Assistant Curator. She retired in 1956 with the title of Associate Curator and as Emeritus continues to serve the Department as consultant on its publications. As the Department's first Wilbour Fellow she published a monograph on *Ancient Egyptian Glass and Glazes in The Brooklyn Museum* in 1968.

In the first decades of the twentieth century the primary intention of The Brooklyn Museum was to serve as an educational institution rather than as an art museum. One aspect of this activity was reflected in the acquisition of scores of plaster casts of famous Greek and Roman sculptures and reliefs. For many years the Classical collection consisted mainly of copies and of electrotypes of coins, including a British Museum series acquired in 1904. It also contained photographs, models and "galvano-plastic" replicas, among them Mycenaean gold vessels from the "Museum of Athens."

Original Classical antiquities came in small gifts, purchases and loans — except for Roman glass vessels, which entered the Museum in a slowly abating stream, passing the 900 mark in 1913. "Ancient gold jewelry" also appeared in generous amounts. The most dramatic early purchase, however, was a group of twenty-one Roman and Jewish mosaics from a synagogue in the "neighborhood of Tunis"; they constitute a unique holding of mosaic art (see p. 99).

As the years passed and the criteria of the Museum's collecting changed from merely didactic to aesthetic, the cast collection of well over 100 pieces experienced many vicissitudes, gradually being replaced by ancient originals.

Objects such as terracotta heads, animals, statues, and lamps came with the original Wilbour bequest in 1916. The finest Minoan vessel, a spouted pitcher that is the best of its type in this country, was part of the Abbott Collection mentioned above (see p. 43). Over the years, other Greek and Roman objects from Egypt or made of uniquely Egyptian materials have enriched the Classical collection.

While the Greek and Roman collection is not endowed, it has had its benefactors. Museum founders, governors, and officers such as A. Augustus Healy and Colonel Robert B. Woodward and their families were generous with loans and gifts during their lifetimes and with benefactions willed to the Museum. Thanks to the munificent gifts of present Museum members, the Department has been able to acquire some handsome gold objects, especially a pair of golden ears of wheat (see p. 83). Through several long-term loans it has been possible to fill in some of the stylistic and chronological gaps of the Classical collection.

The thirties were particularly good to the "Classical Division," one of its several designations during that decade. Some large purchases and important gifts of Greek objects came to the Museum. Most of them, ranging from the Bronze Age to Byzantine times, formed part of the collection of Professor Charles T. Seltman. In 1933, Mlle. Claire Préaux made a survey of the Greek ostraca which resulted in a catalogue published the following year.

Decorated with plaster casts, the "Classical Court" (now the Auditorium Court) was formally opened on November 23, 1934, with the aim of giving "a sense of daily life . . ." At this time, the Classical objects were under the care of Miss Phyllis Williams, who as Mrs. Karl Lehmann was later to become well-known in American archaeology for her work at Samothrace.

The casts were first installed in the West Gallery on the First Floor in 1898. By 1911, the "Greek, Egyptian and Roman Antiquities" were established in Rooms 7 and 8 of the then First Floor where they apparently remained until the opening of the Classical Court in 1934. After the former Classical Gallery was stripped in preparation for the installation of the Assyrian reliefs in 1955, the transfer of modern sculpture to the Fifth Floor freed the Auditorium Court for the exhibition of the Coptic and Classical collections much of which had long been in storage. It is in this Court that they may be seen today, in a slowly but surely expanding exhibition.

Beginning with the great exhibition of "Pagan and Christian Egypt" in 1941, the Department of Ancient Art has presented a number of memorable shows, some of them unique. With the exception of "Greek Gold" (1966) all of these exhibitions originated in the Department, the objects they displayed having been selected and installed by its curatorial staff, who in most instances also provided an illustrated catalogue (see list on pp. 109-110).

Bernard V. Bothmer

Jean L. Keith

CATALOGUE

Bird Deity

From El Ma'mariya, north of
Hierakonpolis*
Painted pottery
Museum Collection Fund

Early Predynastic Period,
about 4000 B.C.
H. 11 $^{7}/_{16}$ in. (29.3 cm)
07.447.505

The first art practiced by man in the ancient Nile Valley was sculpture in the round, and this figure of a female with uplifted arms and a bird's head represents man's earliest attempt to picture tangibly a religious concept, namely that of the spirit of the dead.

Such bird-headed spirits occur in the early religion of many civilizations, always endowed with a human body but with arms raised like wings and with the face of a bird. This figure came to light in a tomb of one of the earliest prehistoric cultures of ancient Egypt, the so-called Amratian Period. It was found in the course of an excavation undertaken on behalf of The Brooklyn Museum by the French scholar Henri de Morgan. Stylized and yet true to nature the statuette reflects an artistic taste of great sophistication.

* Unless otherwise noted, all sites given as provenance are in Egypt.

14

Tripod Vessel

From El Ma'mariya, north of
Hierakonpolis
Red-polished pottery with white design
Museum Collection Fund

Early Predynastic Period,
about 4000 B.C.
H. 6¹/₄ in. (15.9 cm)
07.447.399

At the end of the fifth millennium B.C., when the people of the northern Nile Valley developed a culture which distinguished them from other people of northeast Africa, they entered the last phase of prehistoric existence, which we call the Predynastic Period.

From the beginning of their Predynastic civilization the Egyptians showed a high degree of imagination in the decoration of pottery, both in color and design. They also developed fairly rapidly a great variety of shapes; later the forms of pottery became much simpler. This tripod vessel represents a very rare type: its red-polished surface bears a design in white which combines man-made elements, matting, and patterns found in nature, plant stems.

Vase with Animal Decoration

From Aulad Yahya, near Akhmim
Buff pottery with red painting
Charles Edwin Wilbour Fund
61.87

Late Predynastic Period,
about 3200 B.C.
H. 12⁹/₁₆ in. (32 cm)

The Egyptians, with their innate feeling for color and decoration, produced, strangely enough, painted pottery in only two periods of their long history; from about 4000 to 3200 B.C., and from 1420 to 1300 B.C. This vessel dates from the earlier of the two, at the end of Predynastic times, when a free and easy style of painting was briefly adopted in the decoration of a small group of tall vessels of which less than a dozen examples are known today. No two of them show identical motifs, and yet their characteristics are unmistakable: a procession of animals often interrupted by linear decorations of much elegance.

The upper portion of the Brooklyn vase shows a number of aardvarks, clumsy burrowing animals which no longer exist in Egypt. Although the wiggly lines on the lower part of the vessel may represent snakes, they must be considered primarily a decorative base for the amusing troop that ambles above.

16

Knife of a Hunter

From Abu Zeidan, south of Edfu
Flint and ivory
Museum Collection Fund
09.889.118

Late Predynastic Period,
about 3200 B. C.
Length 9¹/₈ in. (23.2 cm)

The two finest stone knives from ancient Egypt with decorated ivory handles are in the Musée du Louvre and in this Museum. The Louvre piece was acquired in the antiquities market in Cairo; the Brooklyn knife was found in a controlled excavation with the entire contents of its owner's tomb.

The graceful ripples caused by chipping the flint blade are not uncommon, but the rich decoration of the handle demands attention because so little relief decoration has survived from Predynastic times. Numerous rows of animals have been carved with minute care and great delicacy on both sides, and although their arrangement in row upon row is rather formal, it presages the ordered discipline of later Egyptian wall representations. They embody in all probability the fulfillment of what was hoped for by the man in whose tomb the knife had been deposited: an abundance of game to be hunted forever in the hereafter.

The boss is pierced lengthwise, providing a hole through which presumably a string or leather thong was passed so as to secure the weapon to the bearer's wrist.

Female Idol

From Paros (?)

Marble

Museum Collection Fund

35.733

Cycladic, "Developed" or "Keros-Syros"
Type,
third millennium B. C.
H. 11¹/₂ in. (29.5 cm)
W. 5¹¹/₃₂ in. (8.5 cm)

Simplicity was partly imposed on these statuettes by the technical problems of carving the stone. But the nearly flat back, the slightly bent knees and gently swelling forms combined with a bold-nosed face are so persistent as to reflect a conscious choice. The female characteristics — restrained yet clear — identify the figure as a symbol of woman.

Their distribution throughout the Cycladic Islands in the Aegean Sea and even in Asia Minor is an indication of the vast popularity of these figures in antiquity; the very reduction of shapes to the basic minimum results in a monumentality that appeals equally to contemporary artists and connoisseurs. What actual religious meaning they had to their owners is not yet certain, although burial contexts suggest a connection with both birth and death. While the idols are most frequently found laid on their backs in graves, larger examples may have been set up in shrines or dwelling places.

20

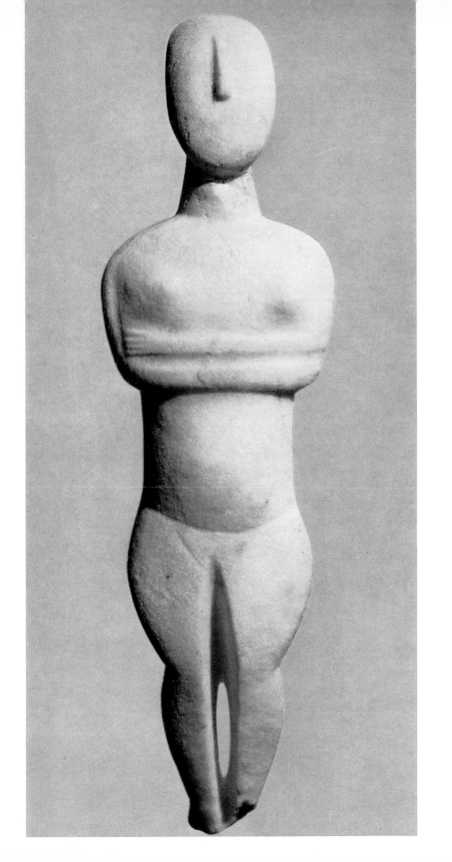

Colossal Head of a King

Red granite
Charles Edwin Wilbour Fund
46.167

Old Kingdom,
late Dynasty III,
about 2600 B. C.
H. 21³/₈ in. (54.3 cm)

Since the beginning of the historical period (about 3150 B. C.) political life of ancient Egypt focused on divine kingship; all activities of the country revolved to a degree hard to define today around the person of the ruler. This position of a god on earth was maintained by Pharaoh for nearly three thousand years, but as society in the Nile Valley grew more complex, the idea of kingship, its concept, and its religious significance were gradually modified.

The earliest representations of Egyptian kings are on a small scale. Not until Dynasty III were statues made which show the ruler lifesize; this forceful head wearing the tall crown of Upper Egypt even surpasses human scale, both in measurements and in its aim to depict the godlike power and strength of the Pharaoh.

The style of the head suggests the period just prior to the rise of Dynasty IV; it is the only one of its kind in hard stone remaining from this period. Its archaic character is underlined by the simplicity of the features which, in their almost brutal directness, are devoid of the kind of sophistication which marks Egyptian statuary of later periods.

Bearded Genius

Diorite
Charles Edwin Wilbour Fund
58.192

Old Kingdom,
late Dynasty III,
about 2600 B.C.
H. 8³/₈ in. (21.3 cm)

The male figure of a Libyan, identified by the knotted belt with phallus sheath poses a problem as to its chronological position. The curious manner in which the knife, held in the right hand, is worked partly in the round and partly in relief, and the absence of an emblematic staff in the left hand relate this statuette to the sculpture of late Dynasty III, rather than of Dynasty V as had been assumed until now. Also the shape of the valanced wig and the back slab favor a date before Dynasty IV.

Still, the identity of the person remains obscure at present. As a Libyan he may represent the local deity of the seventh nome in the Western Delta. As a male deity he personifies an ideal of beauty and virility which was to set an example for several millennia to come.

Inspection of Cattle

From Saqqara

Limestone

Charles Edwin Wilbour Fund

49.62

Old Kingdom, Dynasty V,

about 2420 B. C.

H. 20^1/$_{16}$ in. (51 cm)

Egyptian art can be divided technically into two main fields: one is three-dimensional, and the other two-dimensional. The first consists of sculpture in the round, the latter of relief and painting. Relief work is a kind of modified drawing, either standing out on the background or sunken into the background. The first is called raised relief, the second sunk relief. Here we have a fine example of low raised relief of the Old Kingdom.

Relief work was employed to decorate the temples of the kings and gods of ancient Egypt as well as the tombs of private persons. The decoration consists of ornaments, inscriptions, and especially of representations reflecting the religious beliefs of the dwellers of the Nile Valley and depicting in faithful detail their daily life.

Two servants wearing kilts and an unclad herdsman have brought four heads of prize cattle, to be either inspected or slaughtered. The longhorn breed is neatly labeled by the two hieroglyphs over the animals's back which spell the name of the species, "yuwa." The inscription on the right belongs to a long column of text, the beginning and end of which have been lost; it seems to refer to a series of holy places.

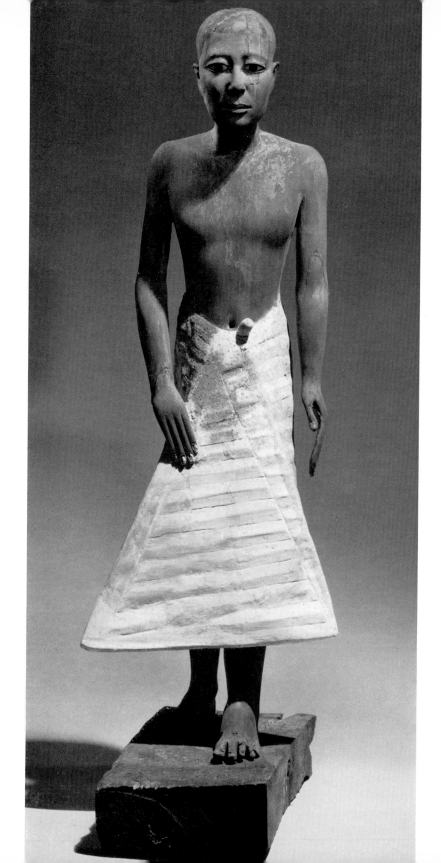

Methethy as a Mature Man

From Saqqara
Wood, covered with gesso and painted
Charles Edwin Wilbour Fund
(see front cover)
51.1

Old Kingdom
early Dynasty VI,
about 2340 B.C.
H. 24^3/$_{16}$ in. (61.5 cm)
Height of head
4^5/$_8$ in. (11.7 cm)

In the collection of The Brooklyn Museum are three statues of an estate administrator named Methethy. The one illustrated is the finest of them, primarily because it shows features far surpassing the idealizing expression which characterizes most Egyptian sculpture. It is the highly individual representation of the face of a sophisticated and intelligent official of ancient Egypt; there is no duplicate and no copy to be found of this figure which indeed approaches true portraiture.

In spite of the perishable material the statue is well preserved; the remarkable elements which make for the highly lifelike expression of the face, namely the eyes, are still in place although they were inlaid with stones within a copper frame and inserted into the sockets ages ago. Their calm gaze endows the face with a human quality that brings the person represented close to the observer and imparts an expression of Methethy's personality, more than four thousand years after this extraordinary likeness was created.

King Pepy II with his Mother

Perhaps from Saqqara
Alabaster
Charles Edwin Wilbour Fund
39.119

Old Kingdom, Dynasty VI,
about 2230 B.C.
H. 15^7/$_{16}$ in. (39.2 cm)

There is no inscribed royal statuary from Dynasty VI preserved intact except for three sculptures in this Museum. One represents King Pepy I in a kneeling attitude, the second shows him seated; by far the most interesting of the group is this statue of Queen Ankhnes-mery-ra holding her son, King Pepy II, on her lap. The sculpture is carved from a single piece of alabaster; the technique is unusual inasmuch as the limbs are for the most part freely modeled in the round instead of being connected to the main mass of the statue by means of "bridges" which were meant to prevent breakage.

The two figures are each strictly frontal, without direct relationship to one another. The composition featuring the large-scale mother with the small-scale boy-king on her lap represents an important departure from the traditional and apparently constitutes an attempt to enrich the repertoire of the statuary. No such group sculpture had ever been made before, and it was to take more than eight hundred years before anything similar was attempted again by an Egyptian artist.

Queen and Hairdresser

From Deir el Bahri (Thebes)
Limestone, with traces of paint
Charles Edwin Wilbour Fund
54.49

Early Middle Kingdom,
Dynasty XI,
about 2030 B. C.
H. 7¹/₂ in (19 cm)

In raised relief (see p. 29) the background is cut away and the representation left standing; in sunk relief the representation is "sunk" into the background which is left untouched. In the brilliant light of Egypt, sunk relief has a far more dramatic effect than low, raised relief; this is probably one of the reasons why it was employed with increasing frequency in the course of Egyptian history.

The crisp, bold style of this relief is typical of the new beginning, which was made at Thebes a century or more after the Old Kingdom had collapsed at the end of Dynasty VI. The fragment came from the underground tomb chamber of Queen Neferu (one of the wives of King Menthu-hotep II), which was carved out of the bedrock below the King's funerary temple at western Thebes.

The Queen is attended by her faithful hairdresser, Henut, who attaches an artificial braid to her mistress' coiffure. Another lock is pinned up with a bodkin to be held out of the way until the new braid has been put into place. The features of queen and hand-maiden are almost identical because they do not represent the individuals named, but reflect the then prevailing ideal female face as carved in the court studios of Menthu-hotep II at Thebes. The prominent nose, the strong indication of the nostril, full lips, and a slanting, highly stylized ear mark unmistakably the characteristic way of cutting relief in the latter part of the reign of this King.

32

33

Monkey Holding on to a Palm Tree

From Abydos
Limestone
Bottom restored
Charles Edwin Wilbour Fund
64.148.1

Middle Kingdom,
Dynasty XII,
about 1950 B.C.
H. 12³/₁₆ in. (31 cm)

There is nothing very definite or certain about this object except that it comes from Egypt, that it shows a monkey clinging to a palm tree (identified as such by the three characteristic ridges on the trunk), and that it is delightful, amusing, and enigmatic. For we do not know what the object really represents, what its purpose was, and in which period it was made. The Middle Kingdom date suggested above is based on smaller parallels from the excavations of the Metropolitan Museum of Art at Lisht, the burial place of the first two kings of Dynasty XII.

But what does it matter? The composition as such (little ape — big tree), the execution (summarily, without much detail), the purpose (not readily understood) — all combine to make this little sculpture an intriguing symbol of the world of ancient Egypt from which so many antiquities have been preserved and of which we still know so little today.

Female Bust

Black mottled granite
Charles Edwin Wilbour Fund
59.1

Middle Kingdom,
early Dynasty XII,
about 1980-1940 B.C.
H. 9⁵/₁₆ in. (23.6 cm)

There is no way of telling who this lady was because the sculpture is devoid of inscription, and the simple costume merely indicates that she was a private person and not of royal rank. With its open, friendly features the face exudes human warmth as well as a positive attitude toward the unknown deity in whose temple the statue was once dedicated. It speaks well for the equality of the sexes in ancient Egypt that a private lady could have a sculpture made for herself.

The heavy tripartite wig frames the broad face and passes behind the ears, thus giving the impression of forcing them forward. They are large in keeping with the ancient Egyptian ideal of beauty; the same ideal required small breasts, and also in this respect the sculpture is no exception. Whereas the natural curve of the eyebrows dips toward the root of the nose, the artificial eyebrows in low relief are absolutely straight above the inner corners of the eyes, a feature which places the bust early in Dynasty XII. Around 1900 B.C. these artificial eyebrows, too, began to follow the natural curve and dipped down toward the nose.

King Sesostris III

From Hierakonpolis
Black granite
Charles Edwin Wilbour Fund
52.1

Middle Kingdom,
Dynasty XII,
1878-1843 B.C.
H. 21¹/₂ in. (54.5 cm)

The sculpture represents Sesostris III, a ruler who left a lasting mark on the history of Egyptian art because he was the first pharaoh of the Nile Valley who had his features modeled in a realistic, rather than idealizing, fashion. Whereas his predecessors, since the early Old Kingdom, were mainly shown with forceful, yet youthful traits, his face is careworn and hard and distinctly shows the signs of age. It is framed by the striped headcloth, the *nemes*, which once bore an uraeus, the royal cobra, above the forehead. In contrast to the energetic, almost brutal features of the face, the torso is rendered in an idealizing manner.

The dominating majesty of an Egyptian pharaoh, who had a statue of himself presented to his god in a sanctuary or temple, is reflected in this dynamic figure which, although seated and looking straight ahead, is full of nervous energy and vibrant strength. There is no humility in the attitude of Sesostris III when facing his god as in this sculpture. A long and wearisome life has left a mark on the King's features which he proudly displays like a badge of honor in the presence of the deity.

39

Squatting Man

Quartzite
Charles Edwin Wilbour Fund
62.77.1

Middle Kingdom,
late Dynasty XII
or early Dynasty XIII,
about 1790-1750 B.C.
H. 27¹/₂ in. (69.8 cm)

With supreme calm this ancient Egyptian nobleman is squatting on the ground, prepared to face his god in the hereafter. He has a cloak wrapped about himself; his left hand rests on his chest in a gesture of devotion.

The broad face, with heavy-lidded eyes and worry lines descending from the corners of the mouth, conveys the impression of a complex personality — quite in contrast to the simplicity of the head-cloth and the highly stylized ears and left hand. This obvious simplicity attracts the observer to the face, and it is most likely that this was done intentionally. The brooding mood of the eyes, the pensive expression, and the almost disdainful mouth seem to characterize the owner better than any outer trappings or even an inscription, although it must be noted that a brief offering formula was once written on top of the base in front of the legs.

Yet it is impossible to identify this man because these same brooding and sorrowful features occur in several other sculptures from the end of Dynasty XII and the beginning of Dynasty XIII; one can therefore assume that these faces constitute a characteristic type of the period, rather than representing the individual features of definite persons.

42

Pitcher with Marine Decoration

Found in Egypt,
originally from
the Island of Crete
Buff-colored terracotta
Abbott Collection,
Charles Edwin Wilbour Fund

Late Minoan Ib,
1500-1425 B. C.
H. 8^{11}/$_{16}$ in. (22 cm)
37.13 E

Around the Aegean Sea a number of pre-Hellenic civilizations had become prominent during the Bronze Age. On Crete, the Minoans led an apparently peaceful and prosperous existence that thrived on their sea-girt island; so attractive was this way of life that the main-land Mycenaeans moved in from the Peloponnesus. That contacts between the island inhabitants and their neighbors in the Eastern Mediterranean were wide-spread is attested to by the fact that this jug was found in Egypt.

Minoan knowledge of the sea was continued by the Mycenaeans in their frequent use of marine forms among the many natural motifs employed in the decoration of beautifully designed utilitarian and decorative objects. The four large creatures on this spouted pitcher are nautiluses (sometimes called argonauts) which jauntily wave their tentacles in a rhythmic if unrealistic fashion. Corals, algae, and other sea life fill every space in an underwater composition bursting with vitality.

A Royal Favorite

From Armant
Gray-black granite
Charles Edwin Wilbour Fund
67.68

New Kingdom,
Dynasty XVIII,
about 1490 B. C.
H. 18⁹/16 in. (47.2 cm)

One of the great personalities of the court of Queen Hatshepsut is represented by this virtually undamaged statue of Senenmut, Chief Steward, Architect, Administrator and confidant of his mistress whose prenomen is incised on his upper right arm.

Although the humility of Senenmut is indicated by his kneeling attitude his exalted position in the society of his day is markedly stressed by the ample folds of his well-rounded body — always a sign of importance in the Middle East — and the fancy wig which frames an intelligent face accented by a prominent nose.

Senenmut proffers the image of a large cobra crowned with cow horns and sun disk that rests on the hieroglyph for *ka*, a raised pair of arms. This assembly was meant as a cryptogram, to be "read" Ma-ka-ra, which is the prenomen of Queen Hatshepsut, Senenmut's royal mistress. The same prenomen occurs also on Senenmut's upper right arm and in the inscription on the back, both times of course written in the clear.

King Amenhotep III

Diorite
Charles Edwin Wilbour Fund
59.19

New Kingdom,
Dynasty XVIII,
about 1405 B. C.
H. 24³/₈ in. (61.9 cm)

This King has been likened to Louis XIV of France because of his splendid court life, his predilection for worldly pleasures, and his unstinting support of the arts which in his time reflected the supreme refinement of royal taste.

When this colossal head was made, probably as part of a coronation statue now lost, the King had just ascended to the throne and may have been no more than twelve or thirteen years old. There is something boyish and yet highly sophisticated in these features which, with the sweeping eyebrows and slanting eyes, were to set a new style of male representation, widely imitated among his courtiers and followers up and down the Nile Valley.

In spite of the vastly over-lifesize scale of the head its features are graceful and elegant. The noble simplicity of the early New Kingdom had long disappeared. Instead, the style changed markedly and became far richer and more varied than ever before — probably thanks to the great influence this King exercised in the decoration of his temples and palaces.

Lady Thepu

Thebes, Tomb no. 181
Painting on gesso over mud plaster
Charles Edwin Wilbour Fund
65.197

New Kingdom,
Dynasty XVIII,
reign of Amenhotep III,
about 1400 B. C.
H. of figure 11⁷/₈ in.
(30.2 cm)

The art of painting was practiced in all great periods of Egyptian art, from the Predynastic age to Roman times. In Dynasty XVIII, it achieved its greatest height, particularly during the reigns of Tuthmosis IV and Amenhotep III. The fragmentary panel of the Lady Thepu dates from the time of the latter king.

She is a well-known personality who appears in several inscriptions and mural paintings in the tomb which her son, the Chief Sculptor Nebamun, shared with another sculptor, probably his predecessor. The woman is dressed in the finery of the great ladies of her time, with a perfumed ointment cone on her heavy wig, the forehead decorated with a diadem, a polychrome collar around her neck, a white shift, and a diaphanous shawl over her shoulders which leaves one breast bare.

The stars over the lady's raised hand are the remains of three columns of text now mostly lost, ending with her name of which the three last signs are still preserved behind the wig. Although a mature woman by the time the mural was painted, she is represented in the glory of eternal youth in keeping with the idealizing style of the time.

Princess Meket-aten

Probably from Tell el Amarna
Brown quartzite
Charles Edwin Wilbour Collection
16.46

New Kingdom,
Dynasty XVIII,
Amarna Period,
about 1370 B.C.
H. 11¼ in. (28.5 cm)

When Charles Edwin Wilbour acquired this fragmentary sculpture at Akhmim in Middle Egypt in 1890, he was told it had been found at Tell el Amarna, the capital of Akhenaten's spiritual kingdom of the Living Sun Disk, the Aten. This provenance is very likely to be correct because the girl whose name appears on the back pillar was the second daughter of King Akhenaten and Queen Nofretity, a princess known to have died at Amarna. The moving scene of mourning for the girl by her parents, as depicted in the royal tomb, is justly famous.

Although today devoid of the head and of most of the limbs, this torso in light brown stone retains much of the lovely figure of the young princess. Her right arm was hanging by her side; the left crosses over below her breasts, and the missing hand probably held a pet bird.

Royal Couple

From Tell el Amarna
Limestone, with traces of paint
Charles Edwin Wilbour Collection
16.48

New Kingdom,
Dynasty XVIII,
Amarna Period,
about 1360 B. C.
H. 6³/₁₆ in. (15.7 cm)

After the sophistication and elegance which mark the style of the reign of King Amenhotep III, a startling change took place early in the reign of his son, Amenhotep IV, who assumed the name of Akhenaten. This new style was highly naturalistic, even realistic in comparison with that of the time of his father, and at the same time the traditional repertoire of subject matter was greatly enlarged.

Akhenaten founded a new capital in honor of his god, Aten, and it was here that Charles Edwin Wilbour acquired this relief on December 22, 1881.

The slab shows the heads of a young royal couple in sunk relief, a king on the left with his queen on the right; for a long time they had been identified as Akhenaten and his consort Nofretity. But all known representations of the famous King depict him with features far more drawn and less youthful. Although the pharaoh shown here slightly resembles Akhenaten, he is undoubtedly a youth and thus must be Akhenaten's son-in-law and successor, King Semenkh-ka-ra.

The same holds true for the head of the queen who, although she wears a cap first encountered in representations of the famous Nofretity, resembles her very little apart from a vague family likeness. Semenkh-ka-ra indeed married Nofretity's daughter, Merit-aten, and it is she who is here most probably represented with her young husband.

52

53

54

Bust of a Nobleman

Painted limestone
Charles Edwin Wilbour Fund
36.261

New Kingdom,
Dynasties XIX-XX,
about 1250-1200 B.C.
H. 20^1/$_2$ in. (52 cm)

The dry elegance of this formal representation of a great official belongs to the Ramesside Period, at the close of the New Kingdom. Despite the splendor of coiffure and garment, the figure represents a man. Carved in sunk relief, the abundance of detail is confined to his attire; the face, far more summarily executed, dominates through the fine delineation of its contour. A few generations later a marked decline set in, and even the faces of kings and noblemen are devoid of all expression; this lasted through the Third Intermediate Period, Dynasties XXI-XXIV (about 1100-720 B.C.).

The scene to which this relief once belonged showed the man probably in the act of offering before the gods. He was followed by his wife or another female member of his household because a hand holds a sistrum, or rattle, which was only used by women in religious processions and other ceremonies.

Openwork Vase

From Upper Egypt
Blue frit
Charles Edwin Wilbour Fund
44.175

Third Intermediate Period,
Dynasties XXI-XXII,
about 1000-800 B. C.
H. 6^{11}/$_{16}$ in. (17 cm)

This famous vase, one of the finest made of this material in ancient Egypt, was once in the MacGregor Collection, but there is no indication where its first owner of record acquired it. First shown at an exhibition of Egyptian art at Burlington House in London in 1895, it has been illustrated several times since as the most elaborate vessel ever made in the long history of ancient Egyptian glassmaking. It was molded of frit, powdered glass that had been made into a paste by adding water, and then fired at a low temperature so that the material became solid without turning into true glass.

The ovoid body of the bottle has a bottom in the form of a lotus flower which is surmounted by deities and mythological symbols. The neck opens into a mouth decorated as a lotus blossom: an elegant crowning, yet so simple in contrast to the fancy work of the vessel's body.

King Osorkon I

From Shibin el Qanatir, near Heliopolis   Third Intermediate Period,
Bronze, solid cast, with gold inlays   Dynasty XXII,
Charles Edwin Wilbour Fund   915-900 B. C.
57.92   H. 5¹/₂ in. (14 cm)

The Third Intermediate Period constitutes a time of transition between the age of Egypt's greatest political power, the New Kingdom,
and the revival during the Late Period, in the wake of the domination by Egypt's Kushite neighbors to the south. Some of the elegance
of the New Kingdom survived, but on the whole sculpture was not
produced in profusion, probably because the centralized power of
great kingship was lacking in Egypt for several hundred years.

It is at this time that bronze, well-known to the Egyptians for
hundreds of years, came more and more into use. They vastly im-
proved on the foreign technique of casting metal sculptures by
perfecting inlay work with gold threads such as is found in this
statuette of King Osorkon I. The inscriptions, the pattern of the
royal kilt, and the figures of the gods which circle the torso of the
pharaoh were all created by cutting into the metal with a sharp
instrument, embedding into the groove a gold thread, and then
hammering the slightly raised surface down so as to be even with
the surrounding area.

Head of Thoëris

Hematite
Charles Edwin Wilbour Fund
58.92

Third Intermediate Period,
Dynasties XXI-XXV,
about 1000-700 B. C.
H. $^{15}/_{16}$ in. (2.4 cm)

The dark and shiny surface of this monster's head reflects the moist element in which the Nile hippopotamus dwells. But this is not a hippo plain and simple; it is the mighty Thoëris, mistress of childbirth and protectress against snakebite and other evil household hazards, who, in the guise of a pregnant hippopotamus with sagging breasts and crocodile's teeth, inspired awe and good will in the women of ancient Egypt.

In the figure now lost she was shown striding, with long strands of hair falling over her shoulders, her ample belly barely supported by short, bandy lion's legs, and her semi-human arms resting on the hieroglyph denoting protection. She is an ugly creature indeed, and yet the crispness of the carving in the extremely hard metallic stone invites detailed observation which in turn arouses admiration from the modern amateur as it must have from the ancient believer.

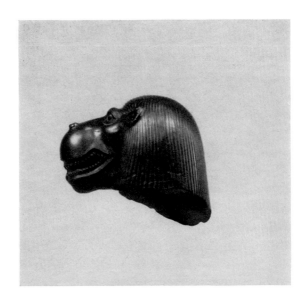

Worshiper with Libation Jars

From Giza
Pale green glassy faience
Abbott Collection
Charles Edwin Wilbour Fund
37.344E

Third Intermediate Period,
Dynasty XXII,
about 900 B.C.
H. 5⁷/₁₆ in. (13.8 cm)

Since the Old Kingdom, Egyptian sculpture frequently depicted a king offering to his god a pair of bowls with water, wine or milk. This statuette, however, does not represent a king, but a chieftain of Libyan mercenaries. As "Great Chief of the Ma" he assumed royal prerogatives, commanding a mercenary corps in the Delta in the times of anarchy between the New Kingdom and the Late Period. His name was Nes-ba-neb-djedet. The quality of the rare material in which the figure is formed is matched by the excellence of the torso modeling.

62

Ashur-nasir-pal II, King of Assyria

From Nimrud, Iraq

Alabastrous limestone

Gift of Hagop Kevorkian

Assyria, about 870 B.C.

H. 7 feet 7¹/₈ in. (2.315 m)

55.155

The twelve large alabaster slabs from the north-west palace of the Assyrian King Ashur-nasir-pal II (883-859 B.C.) at Nimrud form an important section of the Middle Eastern collection of this Museum. The foremost set of such reliefs in this country, they were removed to London in 1853 and two years later brought to Boston where they were acquired by Mr. James Lenox. He presented them to the New-York Historical Society in 1858; in 1937 they were lent to The Brooklyn Museum which in 1955 became the owner through the generosity of the late Mr. Kevorkian.

Here the King is shown in procession, holding in his raised hand a vessel of precious metal and in the other hand a bow. His hair and beard are carefully groomed; a long pendant — probably of gold — adorns his ear, and the haft of a dagger protrudes from under his garment. A long inscription in cuneiform writing extends across the middle of the slab, covering both the King's figure and that of his companion, a winged genius or deity whose raised hand bears an unusual detail, the natural lines of the palm.

64

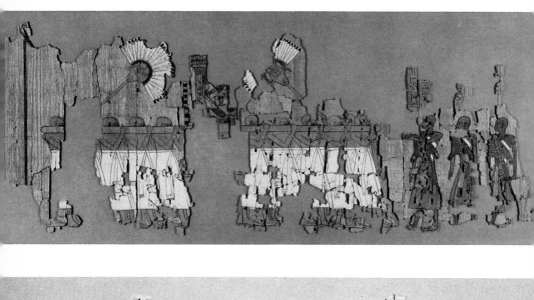

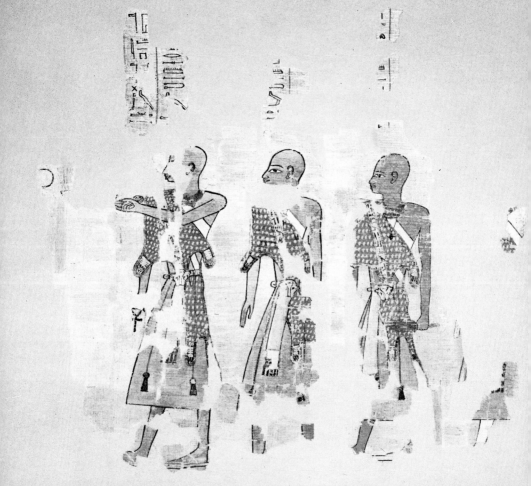

An Historical Painting

From Thebes
Papyrus, painted
Charles Edwin Wilbour Collection
47.218.3

Late Period,
Dynasty XXVI, 651 B. C.
H. 11⅝ in. (29.5 cm)
W. 31¹³/₁₆ in. (80.8 cm)
H. of Mentuemhat 6⁶/₁₆ in.
(16.1 cm)

Among thousands of illustrations in hundreds of papyri preserved from ancient Egypt only one is historical and not religious, that is the scene figured on the right. As far as papyrus vignettes are concerned it is unique.

The illustration forms the beginning of a scroll, a document on papyrus, once about 17 feet long, relating to a procession and an oracle which took place in the Temple of the god Amun-Ra at Karnak on October 4, 651 B. C., in the 14th regnal year of King Psamtik I (664-610 B. C.).

Here the procession is illustrated. Twenty priests are carrying the god's shrine, with one fan bearer before and one after it. The procession is preceded by three, originally eight, dignitaries, the first of whom is well known from many statues and other documents: Mentuemhat, Prince of Thebes, Governor of Upper Egypt, and Fourth Prophet of Amun. He is followed by his son Nes-ptah, Inspector of Prophets in Thebes. After him comes Harkhebe, First Prophet of Amun, who as grandson of the Kushite King Shabaqa (716-702 B. C.) was of Nubian descent and is shown with darker skin.

67

Amphora with Apollo, Leto and Artemis

Said to be from Orticoli, Italy

Black-figure pottery

Bequest of Miss Mary Olcott

62.147.2

Greek, Attic,

about 510 B.C.

H. 15¹³/₁₆ in. (40.2 cm)

The style of pottery decoration that succeeded the Geometric style in Attica is called appropriately "black-figure," because human, animal and plant designs were painted in black glaze on the vase which, when fired, became the familiar reddish color of the background. Details and the exposed flesh of women (faces, arms, feet) were often added in white over the black glaze; sometimes dark red added yet another contrast. Lines incised in the glazed surface indicate modeling of bodies, folds or drapery, and decorative details.

Mythological subjects, gods and goddesses provided popular themes for the many vessels which were in everyday use. On this neck-amphora, Apollo Kitharodos, god of music, strums his *kithara* (lyre) with a *plektron* which is attached to the instrument by a long cord. Leto, mother of Apollo, at right, sniffs a flower; his twin sister Artemis looks over her shoulder to the left. The pet faun of the goddesses completes the group. Each figure wears a long *chiton* (tunic) and an *himation* (cloak) over it.

On the back, two satyrs and a handsome maenad pace and turn in a dance that is surprisingly stately for such followers of Dionysos. The juxtaposition on one vase of the divine symbol of intelligence and light, Apollo, with worshipers of the god of fertility, drink and the dark and irrational as aspects of human life is a striking one.

68

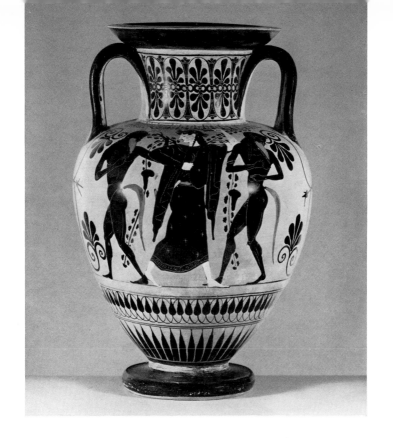

70

Persian Guard

From the Apadana at Persepolis
Grey limestone
Gift of The Kevorkian Foundation
65.195

Persia, about 486-480 B. C.,
reign of Xerxes
H. 10¼ in. (26.1 cm)

The soldier, bearing a shield and once carrying a spear, is one of a long file of royal guards that marched solemnly across a parapet of the audience hall in the palace at Persepolis. This fragment probably comes from the center of the west face of the parapet bordering the central landing.

Appropriately, these guardians decorated the landing of the Apadana (audience hall), embodying the nobility and strength of the *Ten Thousand Immortals,* the cream of the Achaemenid army, which conquered the lands bordering the Eastern Mediterranean. While other members of this corps are shown with bow and quiver as well as the lance, all wore their hair in uniformly curled locks, under the *cidaris,* the tall fluted headgear, and were dressed in long flowing robes.

This kind of low relief was much favored by the Persians and, although based on Assyrian prototypes, could hardly have been executed on such a vast scale by Achaemenid workmen. Ionian Greek and even Egyptian craftsmen may have helped, which accounts for some of the sophistication in these representations reflecting an international rather than provincial Persian style.

Lion Vessel

Probably from Leontopolis, Lower Egypt
Alabaster
Charles Edwin Wilbour Fund
53.223

Late Period,
Dynasty XXVII,
525-404 B. C.
H. 4³/₁₆ in. (10.6 cm)

With the first period of Persian domination, from the late sixth to the fifth century B.C., numerous artistic and political accomplishments of the ancient Middle East were brought to Egypt by the conquering Achaemenids. Although Egyptian statuary was not directly affected, costumes and ornaments employed by the Persians were frequently adapted to native taste by Egyptian artisans. A good example is the little lion, here shown holding an ointment vessel, with numerous cutout depressions carved in his skin — a form of surface ornamentation which hitherto had been foreign to Egyptian art. These cutouts once held polychrome inlays which must have enhanced the yellow-and-white alabaster to startling effect.

One of a small group of lions holding vessels, all found in the Delta, this little figure was most likely used in a temple ritual. Its place of origin presumably was a great temple dedicated to the Egyptian deity Mahes, a lion god much venerated by the Persians when they came to the Nile Valley.

Amphora with the Death of Orpheus

From Vulci, Italy
Red-figure pottery
Museum Collection Fund
59.34

Attic, about 470 B.C.,
attributed to the Niobid Painter
H. with cover 20^{15}/$_{16}$ in. (53.2 cm)

Amphorae were used for many centuries in Greece and throughout the Mediterranean world for storage and transportation of liquid and solid provisions. This ovoid shape with a distinct joining between body and neck of the vessel is called a neck-amphora and was often covered with a lid, wheel-made as was the vase itself. The red-figure painting technique, developed in the later part of the sixth century B.C., reserves the figures in the red color of the fired clay and covers the background with shiny black glaze.

74

Orpheus, the consummate musician, is traditionally connected with Thrace, in northern Greece. His musical artistry charmed all living things but was also, perhaps indirectly, the cause of his death. According to one tradition, the women of Thrace, angered by their husbands' attention to Orpheus' cult, tore him limb from limb. It is these women who are represented by the lady brandishing a household spit to attack the musician as he sits in the rocky landscape.

A bearded man and a youth are making an offering at an altar on the back of the vase. The grapes and the wine cup held by the cloaked man may refer to another version of the death of Orpheus which implicated Dionysos with the Thracian women.

Ibex Handle

From Tell el Maskhuta, Eastern Delta
Silver
Charles Edwin Wilbour Fund
54.50.41

Late Dynasty XXVII,
about 410 B.C.
H. 6⁹/₁₆ in. (16.7 cm)

Near the site of Biblical Pithom, in the Land of Goshen, mercenaries of north Semitic origin served as frontier guards when the Persians dominated Egypt from 525 to 404 B.C. There was a temple on the site dedicated to the Semitic goddess Alat, and from the treasure of its sanctuary the Museum has a set of fine silver vessels and ornaments in gold and semiprecious stones which combine Achaemenid and Egyptian elements.

The handle of one of these vessels is fashioned in the shape of a jumping ibex with forelegs folded under and the hind legs extended along the stem of the handle. Although Persian in style this piece probably was made locally by an Egyptian artisan since it so obviously reflects the solidity of Egyptian sculpture rather than the lithe elegance of Achaemenid workmanship of the fifth century B.C.

78

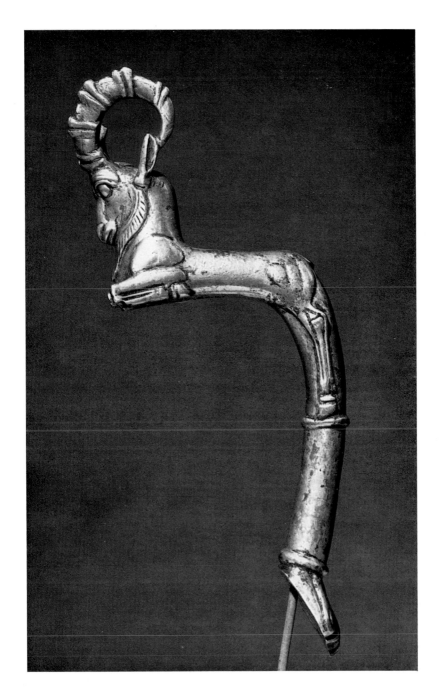

Head of Wesir-wer

From Karnak
Green schist (metamorphic slate)
Charles Edwin Wilbour Fund
55.175

Late Period,
Dynasty XXX,
about 360 B.C.
H. 5⁷/₈ in. (15 cm)

Wesir-wer was Chief of the Prophets of the God Monthu at Thebes. The head of his statue has been in The Brooklyn Museum for more than ten years whereas the body was discovered about sixty years ago at the Temple of Amun in Karnak, at Thebes, and has been in the Cairo Museum ever since.

This is probably the best individual likeness sculptured in Egypt in the fourth century B.C. and undoubtedly was modeled from life. The unwrinkled mask of skin, stretched tightly over the bone structure, presents a face of great intelligence and — especially around the mouth — determination. Made a generation before Alexander the Great conquered Egypt in 332 B.C., the head shows not the slightest trace of Greek influence. On the contrary, it presents a classic example of the archaistic tendencies for which Dynasty XXX is well known. Simplicity in the structure of the face and sparing means employed in modeling the features are characteristic of this period. As the best example of this type of portraiture, the head of Wesir-wer stands stylistically about midway between the realistic likenesses of the early Persian Period and the greatest portrait of the Ptolemaic Period, the "Green Head" in Boston.

80

Ears of Wheat

Probably from North Greece
Gold
Gift of Mr. and Mrs. Carl L. Selden
and Mrs. Frank K. Sanders
67.13

Second half of the
fourth century B.C.
H. 8⁷/₈ in. (22.5 cm)

Wheat, now cultivated in many parts of the world, probably originated in the Zagros Mountains of Iran and spread to the lands surrounding the eastern end of the Mediterranean Sea.

As centuries passed, wheat became a staple food and an important trade commodity. Because of their dependence on this basic crop, the Greeks associated it with the goddess Demeter who was their mother goddess and goddess of agriculture. The wheat itself symbolized the hope of rebirth and of plentiful harvest.

These two golden stalks of wheat were created during the fourth century B.C., possibly for burial with a priestess of Demeter. They are made from many small pieces of gold, each one shaped with simple hand tools. The hollow kernels are ingeniously attached to the stems with very fine wires. The composite pieces are of exquisite workmanship, the results of the skill of a master craftsman. The realistic and graceful appearance of these stalks is typical of the perfection achieved in the art of goldsmithing during the Hellenistic Period.

Votive Head

Found in Cerveteri, Italy, in 1826
Terracotta
By exchange with the Vatican
62.66

Etruscan, first half of
third century B. C.
H. 10 $^{15}/_{16}$ in. (27.8 cm)
W. 7$^{1}/_{16}$ in. (18 cm)

International cooperation among museums is always mutually bene-
ficial. This clay head of a woman is the result of one such exchange.

In 1961, an Egyptologist discovered that an Egyptian head in The
Brooklyn Museum had originally been part of a statue in the Vatican collection. Since major institutions are rarely free to dispose
outright of objects in their care, an exchange was arranged between
the two museums. The head was sent to the Vatican, which in turn
offered to Brooklyn an Etruscan sculpture of a type and period not
represented here thus far.

The half-head, hollow with a round vent hole in the center back,
may have stood against or hung on a temple wall. It was probably
a votive offering. The major contours were formed in a mold, and
the fine details were added by hand before firing. The arrangement
of the hair and the aloof, idealized expression suggest that a goddess
is represented. Still, heads of human women were also modeled in
the round in clay and incorporated into the elaborate architectural
decoration of wooden Etruscan temples.

King and Goddess

Basalt
Charles Edwin Wilbour Fund
62.46

Ptolemaic Period,
3rd century B. C.
H. 7³/₄ in. (19.7 cm)

Here is a scene of two figures of equal height and equal importance, a goddess on the left and a king on the right, surmounted by the starstudded hieroglyph meaning "sky." The slim figure of the deity has a caption which calls her "Hathor, Mistress of the Southern Sycamore Tree," a sacred tree known to have been venerated at Memphis since the third millennium B. C.

In thousands of years the image of the goddess had not changed: she was still pictured as the beautiful female, wearing a crown of cow horns with the sun disk on her head. The king, who is presenting her with two ritual rattles, is probably Ptolemy II (285-246 B. C.). In the column of inscription below his hands he addresses her as his mother, and she in turn, in the text below her outstretched arm holding the scepter, promises him divine "endowment."

The purpose of the relief is somewhat of a puzzle; it could hardly have been an ex-voto since the edges would not have been left in the rough. Thus one can only surmise that it formed part of the decoration of a shrine covered with numerous similar scenes of king and deity which was broken up before it had been completed. The workmanship is unusually careful and finely executed, considering the small scale and the hardness of the material.

86

88

Alexander the Great

Egyptian alabaster
Charles Edwin Wilbour Fund
54.162

Hellenistic,
second century B. C.
H. 3^{9}/$_{16}$ in. (9 cm)

Around the middle of the fourth century B. C. a young Greek king from Macedonia, Alexander, soon to be called the Great, consolidated the Greek states under his leadership and went on to conquer most of the Middle East. He thus extended the influence of Hellenic civilization to Africa and far into Asia. In Egypt he founded the city which still bears his name and which, within a century, became one of the great centers of Hellenistic culture.

While he was still alive Alexander was already worshiped as a god, and his likenesses in stone and metal were widely distributed throughout his empire. Long after his death fine portraits of the youthful and vigorous hero continued to be produced throughout the Hellenistic world.

This portrait bust in Alexandrian style may have been combined with other materials to form a complete figure. Attachment holes around the head indicate that it wore a crown or diadem, probably of gold. The intense upward gaze, the luxuriant hair, and the emotional expression of the mouth are characteristic of the later, idealized representations that have kept alive the memory of Alexander the Great, of his exploits and vivid personality.

90

The "Brooklyn Black Head"

From Mitrahineh (Memphis)
Black diorite
Charles Edwin Wilbour Fund
58.30

Late Ptolemaic Period,
about 80 B. C.
H. 16¼ in. (41.4 cm)

Among the great Egyptian portraits of the Late Period, the "Brooklyn Black Head" represents a sculpture with both Egyptian and Hellenistic elements. The heroic scale, the strict frontality, and the inscription on the back pillar are in the pharaonic tradition; whereas the curly hair, the wide open eyes, and the high degree of asymmetry of the features are due to Greek influence.

This is a portrait in the best sense of the word. It does not represent a type, but the modeling seems to follow faithfully the individual features of a definite person, rendering both the physical likeness and something of the quality of his inner personality.

The man immortalized in the "Brooklyn Black Head," though anonymous at present, was undoubtedly a high-ranking official, possibly even the Governor of Memphis in the declining years of Ptolemaic rule. Stylistically the sculpture is datable to about 80 B.C., and thus the portrayed may well have served Ptolemy XII, father of Cleopatra VII, or even the eminent Queen herself.

Head of Sarapis

Glassy faience
Charles Edwin Wilbour Fund
58.79.1

Alexandrian,
first century A. D.
H. 4 in. (10.1 cm)

When the Ptolemies, successors to Alexander the Great, assumed government of the Greek communities in Egypt, they established an official god who combined both Greek and Egyptian qualities in order to appeal to native Egyptians as well as to the Greek settlers. The god, Sarapis, had properties of Osiris, Egyptian god of the underworld, and of the bull Apis, his earthly incarnation, while many of his powers and characteristics were identified with Zeus and the healer Asklepios. As the cult spread through the Eastern Mediterranean, Sarapis cult shrines were frequently related to Isis sanctuaries; under the Empire, they extended throughout the entire Roman world.

The luxuriant beard and hair are characteristic of Sarapis — especially the locks springing up from the center of the forehead. Behind the front rows of curls is a broad flat band, and on top of the head, a roughly circular broken place was probably the base of an attribute. In the case of Sarapis, it would have been either bovine horns, or a *modius* or basket-shaped corn measure appropriate to the fertility aspects of the god.

Trained Bear

From Egypt   Roman,
Bronze   first century A. D.
Charles Edwin Wilbour Fund   H. $3^7/_8$ in. (9.8 cm)
58.97

With his forepaws raised, the squat little bear seems to have just sat down after performing a dance at the urging of his trainer. Such scenes are not unknown on the streets of Near Eastern cities even in modern times.

The leafy, wreath-like collar masks the joint of the "lid," which is the top of the head from the upper jaws, with a hinge at the back of the neck. With the lid raised, the benign beast appears more to be yawning than roaring. Two loops at the lower edge of the collar and under the ears were probably used for fastening the lid or suspending the vessel by cords. The receptacle may have been a container for liquid pigment or perfume, for medicine or even for bear fat that was used in ancient times in cosmetics and pharmacology.

Boy of Isis Cult

From El Rubiyat, Fayum
Tempera on cypress wood panel
Charles Edwin Wilbour Fund
41.848

Coptic; Roman Period,
about A. D. 300-350
H. 11³/4 in. (30.2 cm)

The practice of incorporating an image of the human face into mummy coverings reaches far back into earliest Egyptian burial customs. Modeled in plaster or in cartonnage and later painted on flat, wooden panels wrapped over the mummy's face, these portraits represent the deceased in variously stylized or realistic fashions. The large eyes and the direct and solemn mien of this youth are extensions of the tradition of earlier mummy masks.

The young boy in this painting is an acolyte of the Isis cult. He grasps a cup and a garland as emblems of his religious belief and wears the side hairlock long associated with the child-god Horus. Worship of Isis, sister and consort of Osiris and mother of Horus, was modified as it was assimilated by the Greeks and later by the Romans when they occupied Egypt. Often associated with the worship of Serapis, Isis cults spread throughout the Mediterranean countries and persisted well into the sixth century A. D.

Two Roman Mosaics

From Hammam Lif, Tunisia
Stone mosaic
Museum Collection Fund
upper: 05.29
lower: 05.26

Third to fifth century A. D.
upper: Diam. 21^1/$_8$ in. (53.6 cm)
lower: H. 22^5/$_8$ in. (57.4 cm)
W. 34^{15}/$_{16}$ in. (88.8 cm)

In 1883, in the main sanctuary of a synagogue in a Tunisian town, a French army officer discovered a mosaic pavement composed of several sections. Twenty parts of this pavement were taken to Paris and thence, in 1905, brought to this Museum. It has been possible to piece together the general composition of the entire mosaic from the sections in the Museum and from the sketches made by the soldier who found them, in spite of the fact that the whereabouts of many fragments are unknown.

Several round medallions include heads of animals and humans. They are made in an especially fine mosaic technique called *opus vermiculatum;* the tesserae are small and irregularly shaped but skilfully arranged so as to indicate the modeling of the shoulder, breast and drapery of the lady.

The pensive woman represented here may be Minerva, but is more likely an Amazon, one of the mythical warrior maidens of Asia Minor who were perpetual opponents of the ancient Greeks.

Other mosaics of this group, representing a variety of natural creatures, plants, and symbolic objects, are constructed in *opus tessellatum,* or stone cubes of fairly equal size set in a cement binder. The palette is muted, restricted to the colors of natural stones.

The seven-branched candlestick, the menorah, became in Roman times one of the predominant symbols of Judaism. It is incorporated into several ancient Jewish mosaics in buildings in Palestine and other sites bordering the Eastern and Southern Mediterranean.

The One Cured of Paralysis

From Sheikh Ibada (Antinoöpolis),
Upper Egypt
Limestone, with traces of polychromy
Charles Edwin Wilbour Fund

Coptic; Roman Period,
about A. D. 400
H. 24$^{1}/_{4}$ in. (61.5 cm)
62.44

This statue, representing a man who is rising to carry his bed, is one of the few examples in Coptic art which illustrates a Biblical subject in sculpture in the round on a large scale. The figure is that of the Paralytic whose miraculous cure is related in the New Testament (Matthew 9:5, Mark 2:11, Luke 5:24) when he was told by Christ: "Arise, and take up thy bed, and go into thine house."

The fact that he is shown naked is unusual because the subject occurs occasionally in early Christian art where the Paralytic invariably is dressed in a simple tunic with a cord around his waist. But Upper Egypt, where this sculpture was created, is distant from the centers of early Christian iconography, and thus the subject of the Paralytic's body — the physical appearance of the sick now cured — has been approached in a somewhat primitive manner.

Woman with Cross

From Sheikh Ibada (Antinoöpolis),
Upper Egypt
Limestone
Charles Edwin Wilbour Fund

Coptic; Roman Period,
fourth century A. D.
H. 14 in. (35.6 cm)
63.36

The Coptic Period of Egypt comprises the centuries of declining Graeco-Roman and rising Christian civilizations in the Nile Valley; its art employed both Hellenistic-Roman subjects and Christian motifs. Human figures with identifiable Christian symbols such as the cross are unusual.

The open face and wide eyes characterize the simple, direct manner of representation which is typical of Coptic art. Since it expresses the sentiments of the native lower and middle classes, and not those of the Romans who administered Egypt at that time, it lacks sophistication and reflects a kind of naive provincialism which is also found in the architecture and literature of the Copts.

The strict frontality of the lady's pose is, of course, a feature directly derived from ancient Egyptian statuary. In spite of the stylistic link with an old artistic tradition, the purpose and meaning of the statue are not all clear. It may represent a saint or martyr or perhaps a worshipful lady who donated an image of herself to her parish church or to a sanctuary to which she made a pilgrimage.

Tapestry Hanging with Figures

From Egypt
Wool
Charles Edwin Wilbour Fund
46.128

Early seventh century A. D.
H. 51³/₁₆ in. (103 cm)
W. 57⁷/₈ in. (147 cm)

Figures in arcades are not uncommon in textiles of this period; that there was at least one more row of figures above the two preserved, indicates how large the original must have been. Comparison with a similar, excavated piece in Brussels suggests that our tapestry may once have hung in a tomb.

The garments of the figures are varied and easily recognized. Four of the persons (one top right and three bottom right) wear simple Classical or Coptic tunics. At upper left is a man who wears what seems to be a Persian Sasanian costume — a long, skirted coat over trousers. The man wearing an animal skin (lower left) may be the hero Herakles or perhaps a follower of Dionysos; he surely must have Classical connections. The hands of the two central figures of the present top arcade are covered with their long sleeves, as is one of each of four other figures. This tradition continued in Christian iconography for the offering of gifts to the Madonna by attendant saints. All but two of the figures have nimbuses behind their heads, another symbol well known in Christian iconography. The presence of two non-Christian figures in this context makes the interpretation of the group problematic.

SELECTED BIBLIOGRAPHY

Ancient Egypt

Aldred, Cyril. *The Development of Ancient Egyptian Art* . . . (London, Tiranti, 1952)

Aldred, Cyril. *The Egyptians* (New York, Praeger, 1961) = *Ancient Peoples and Places* 18

Kees, Hermann. *Ancient Egypt; A Cultural Topography* (London, Faber & Faber, 1961)

Lange, Kurt, and Hirmer, Max. *Egypt; Architecture, Sculpture, Painting in Three Thousand Years*, 4th rev. ed. (London, New York, Phaidon, 1968)

Mertz, Barbara. *Red Land, Black Land; The World of the Ancient Egyptians* (New York, Coward-McCann, 1966)

Posener, Georges. *Dictionary of Egyptian Civilization.* With the assistance of Serge Sauneron and Jean Yoyotte (New York, Tudor, 1962)

Smith, William Stevenson. *The Art and Architecture of Ancient Egypt* (Baltimore, Penguin Books, 1958) = *The Pelican History of Art*, v. 14

Ancient Greece and Rome

Becatti, G. *Art of Ancient Greece and Rome* (New York, Abrams, 1968)

Boardman, J. et. al. *Greek Art and Archaeology* (New York, Abrams, 1967)

Boardman, J. *Pre-Classical Greece: From Crete to Archaic Greece* (Baltimore, Penguin, 1968)

Kähler, H. *The Art of Rome and Her Empire* (New York, Crown, 1965)

Mansuelli, G. A. *The Art of Etruria and Early Rome* (New York, Crown, 1965)

Richardson, E. *The Etruscans: Their Art and Civilization* (Chicago, Univ. of Chicago Press, 1964)

Schefold, K. *The Art of Classical Greece* (New York, Crown, 1967)

Toynbee, J. *The Art of the Romans* (New York, Praeger, 1965)

Webster, T. B. L. *The Art of Greece: The Age of Hellenism* (New York, Crown, 1966)

Ancient Middle East

AKURGAL, E. *The Art of the Hittites* (London, Thames and Hudson, 1962)

FRANKFORT, H. *The Art and Architecture of the Ancient Orient* (Baltimore, Penguin Books, 1955) = *Pelican History of Art*, v. 27

KENYON, K. *Archaeology in the Holy Land* (New York, Praeger, 1960)

MALLOWAN, M. E. L. *Early Mesopotamia and Iran* (New York, McGraw-Hill, 1965)

MELLAART, J. *The Earliest Civilizations in the Near East* (New York, McGraw-Hill, 1966)

PORADA, E. *The Art of Ancient Iran; Pre-Islamic Cultures* (New York, Crown, 1965)

STROMMENGER, E., and HIRMER, M. *5000 Years of the Art of Mesopotamia* (New York, Abrams, 1964)

108

PUBLICATIONS

Department of Ancient Art
1933-1968

Titles listed with asterisk and price can be obtained postpaid from The Gallery Shop, The Brooklyn Museum, Brooklyn, New York 11238. The other titles are out of print.

Catalogue of the Egyptological Library and Other Books from the Collection of the Late Charles Edwin Wilbour, compiled by William Burt Cook, Jr. (1924)

Short Guide to the Charles Edwin Wilbour Egyptological Collections, by Edwin L. M. Taggart (1933)

Les ostraca grecs de la collection Charles-Edwin Wilbour au Musée de Brooklyn [by Claire Préaux] (1935)

Wilbour, Charles Edwin. *Travels in Egypt [December 1880 to May 1891]; Letters of Charles Edwin Wilbour*, edited by Jean Capart (1936) 614 p., illus.

Pagan and Christian Egypt; Egyptian Art from the First to the Tenth Century A.D., Exhibited at The Brooklyn Museum by the Department of Ancient Art, January 23 - March 9, 1941 (1941)

* - - -. Reprint of the 1941 edition (New York, Arno Press Inc., 1969) 200 p., 167 illus. on 107 plates $15.00

The Wilbour Papyrus, edited by Alan H. Gardiner. 4 vols. (London, published for The Brooklyn Museum by Oxford University Press, 1941-1952)

       Vol. 1 = *Plates, Facsimiles and Hieroglyphic Transcription*

       Vol. 2 = *Commentary*

       Vol. 3 = *Translation*

       Vol. 4 = *Index*, by Raymond O. Faulkner

Late Egyptian and Coptic Art; An Introduction to the Collection in The Brooklyn Museum (1943) 24 p., 79 illus. on 54 plates

Toilet Articles from Ancient Egypt, from the Charles Edwin Wilbour Memorial Collection and the Collection of the New-York Historical Society in The Brooklyn Museum [by Elizabeth Riefstahl] (1943)

Coptic Egypt; Papers Read at a Symposium Held under the Joint Auspices of New York University and The Brooklyn Museum, February 15, 1941, in Connection with the Exhibition, Paganism and Christianity in Egypt, Shown at The Brooklyn Museum, January 23 to March 9, 1941 (1944)

Riefstahl, Elizabeth. *Patterned Textiles in Pharaonic Egypt* (1944)

Riefstahl, Elizabeth. *Glass and Glazes from Ancient Egypt* (1948)

Egyptian Art in The Brooklyn Museum Collection (1952)

People of the Black Land, Egypt, compiled by Elizabeth Riefstahl (1952)

    Series I, *The Country and the People*, 6 parts $.50

    Series II, *Egyptian Writing*, 4 parts $.30

Kraeling, Emil G. *The Brooklyn Museum Aramaic Papyri; New Documents of the Fifth Century B.C. from the Jewish Colony at Elephantine* (1953)

* - - -. Reprint of the 1953 edition (New York, Arno Press Inc., 1969) xv, 319 p., 44 illus. on 25 plates, 6 text figs. $18.00

Hayes, William C. *A Papyrus of the Late Middle Kingdom in The Brooklyn Museum (Papyrus Brooklyn 35.1446)* (1955) 165 p., 14 plates

Five Years of Collecting Egyptian Art, 1951-1956; Catalogue of an Exhibition Held at The Brooklyn Museum, 11 December, 1956 to 17 March, 1957 (1956)

* - - -. Reprint of the 1956 edition (New York, Arno Press Inc., 1969) 63 p., 170 illus. on 96 plates $15.00

Egyptian Sculpture of the Late Period; 700 B.C. to A.D. 100. Catalogue compiled by Bernard V. Bothmer in collaboration with Herman De Meulenaere and Hans Wolfgang Müller. Edited by Elizabeth Riefstahl (1960)

* - - -. Reprint of the 1960 edition with 4-page listing of addenda, corrigenda and additional bibliography (New York, Arno Press Inc., 1969) xxxix, 197 p., 356 illus. on 135 plates $20.00

*Cooney, John D. *Amarna Reliefs from Hermopolis in American Collections* (1965) 110 p., 79 illus., 2 color plates $8.00

*Hoffmann, Herbert, and Davidson, Patricia F. *Greek Gold; Jewelry from the Age of Alexander,* edited by Axel von Saldern (1965) xi, 311 p., 264 illus. (incl. figures), 8 color plates and 1 map $4.95

**The Pomerance Collection of Ancient Art [Catalogue of an Exhibition Held at The Brooklyn Museum June 14 to October 2, 1966].* Preface by Jean L. Keith, foreword by Charles K. Wilkinson, catalogue by Edward L. B. Terrace, Bernard V. Bothmer, Jean L. Keith, G. M. A. Hanfmann, David G. Mitten (1966) 127 p., 143 illus, 4 color plates $4.50

*Riefstahl, Elizabeth. *Ancient Egyptian Glass and Glazes in The Brooklyn Museum* (1968) = Wilbour Monographs I. xv, 118 p., 100 illus., 26 color illus. on 13 plates $9.00

GUIDES TO THE BROOKLYN MUSEUM

1 *The Jan Martense Schenck House,* by Marvin D. Schwartz, 1964

2 *Art of the Eastern Plain Indians. The Nathan Sturges Jarvis Collection,* by Norman Feder, 1964

3 *The Emily Winthrop Miles Collection. The Work of Wedgwood and Tassie,* by Jean Gorley and Marvin D. Schwartz, 1965

4 *American Interiors 1675-1885. A Guide to the American Period Rooms in The Brooklyn Museum,* by Marvin D. Schwartz, 1968

5 *Brief Guide to the Department of Ancient Art, 1970*

Hedgehog, Faience
Middle Kingdom
Charles Edwin Wilbour Fund
65.2.1